THE BRAMBLEBERRYS ANIMAL ALPHABET

Created by
Marianna Mayer
and
Gerald McDermott

A RIVERBANK PRESS BOOK

LONGMEADOW PRESS

A

APES

APPLES

B

**BEAR
BLOWING
BLUE
BUBBLES**

C

CHEESE

CUTTING

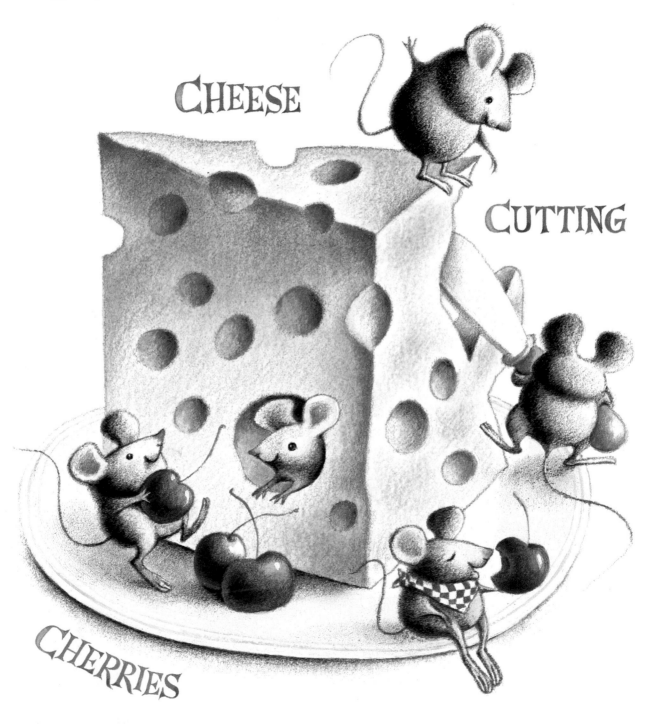

CHERRIES

F FROLICKING

FROGS

FISHING

G

GIRAFFE

GRASS

H

HAT

HIVE

HONEY

ICE SKATING

ICICLES

J

JUMPING

JUMPING

JUMPING

K

KITE

KISS
KISS

L

LICKING
LOLLIPOPS

LICK
LICK

LION

M

N NIGHT

O

OWLS

P

PANDA

PEELING
PEAR

Q

QUAILS

QUIET

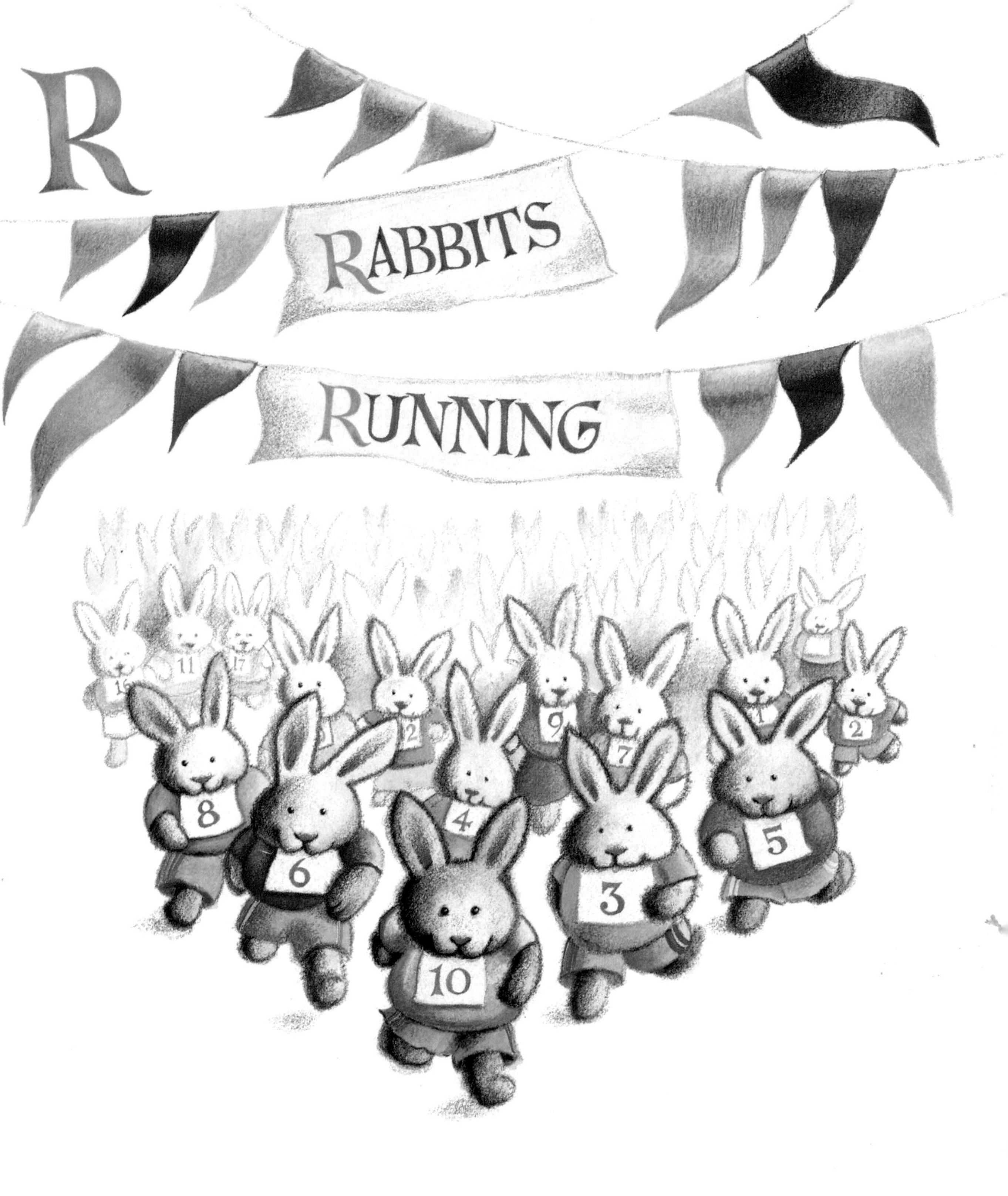
R
RABBITS
RUNNING

T

TINY TIGER'S TEAR

V

VEGETABLES

Z

ZEBRA

For Anna Elizabeth

A RIVERBANK PRESS BOOK

This edition produced for
LONGMEADOW PRESS
201 High Ridge Road
Stamford, CT 06904

Printed and bound in Hong Kong/Jade Productions, Ltd.
THE BRAMBLEBERRYS is a Trademark of Riverbank Press

ISBN 0-681-40160-5